First published 2010 by Modern Toss Ltd.
Modern Toss, PO Box 386, Brighton BN1 3SN, England
www.moderntoss.com

ISBN 978-0-9564191-1-8

The Desperate Business cartoons first appeared in Private Eye

Text and illustrations copyright © Modern Toss Limited, 2010
PO Box 386, Brighton BN1 3SN, England

A CIP catalogue record for this book is available
from the British Library.

Designed and typeset by Modern Toss
Printed and bound by Proost Belgium

Visit www.moderntoss.com to read more about all our books and to buy them yeah.
You will also find lots of other shit there, and you can sign up for e-newsletters so that
you're always first to hear about our new releases.

MODERN TOSS PRESENTS

by Jon Link and Mick Bunnage

work

yeah it's a bit quiet this morning, I've just been googling
my name, 'Steve's' pretty common apparently

interview

work

according to our data, you logged into your facebook page 282 times yesterday
how d'you know it was me?

interview

key strategy meeting

first item, Peter would like to apologise for his absence, says he couldn't be fucked

written warning

work

I'm applying to go on The Apprentice next year,
can you give me a reference confirming that I'm capable
of bollocksing up really basic tasks to a very high standard

interview

genuine enquiry

If I feel ill on holiday can I claim it back as a sick day?

careers advice

work experience

interview

interview

work

hello is that maintenance? yeah temperature wise I'm ok but I think the noise levels are contravening european guidelines

long shot

liquid breakfast

just checking what the company guidelines are for coming in pissed

work

job shadow

work

interview

work

work

worth a punt

work experience

this month's courier bill has 25 pickups from your home address

it's me mum's fault she never has me sandwiches ready when I leave in the morning

work

over-confident applicant

work experience

written warning

interview

desperate business

I'm afraid we're going to have to cut your hours

Not a problem, any chance you could cut out the ones
between my lunch hour and when I go home?

maverick boss

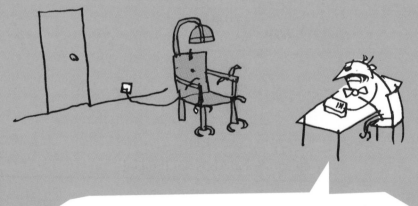

Jean, choose someone at random and send them in please

work

worth a punt

fucking time wasters

desperate business

we're exploring new business opportunities.
Carry on with the accounts but every time
that red light goes on slip your top off

desperate business

work experience

work

work

work experience

interview

work

work

work experience

work experience

work experience

desperate salesman

careers advice

data analyst

work

Hello is that Microsoft? yeah half the words I'm thinking about using aren't even in your spellcheck, you got anything a bit more up to date?

commuter meltdown

good journey in?

yeah not bad, I pushed some bloke under a train

interview

desperate business

and I see here you went to Cambridge

yeah I had to drop something off for someone, I was back by half six

new start